For Mojo and all the smiley snorty pugs that light up the world.

Cover Art by Nadine Rebrovic
Design and Distribution by Bublish

ISBN: 978-1-64704-273-8 (paperback)
ISBN: 978- 978-1-64704-274-5 (hardcover)

HOW TO LOVE YOUR PUG

10 SIMPLE RULES
FOR LOVING YOUR PUG
WITH ALL OF YOUR
MIGHTY HEART

WRITTEN BY LISA BLAKE
ILLUSTRATED BY NADINE REBROVIC

There are

10 simple rules

for loving your pug

with all of your mighty heart.

First, treats.

Always have the treats.

Stock your cupboards, your pockets, the car and your backpack with your pug's favorite yummy snacks.

Next, lots of naps and snuggles.

Be ready at any moment to curl up and cuddle your pug.

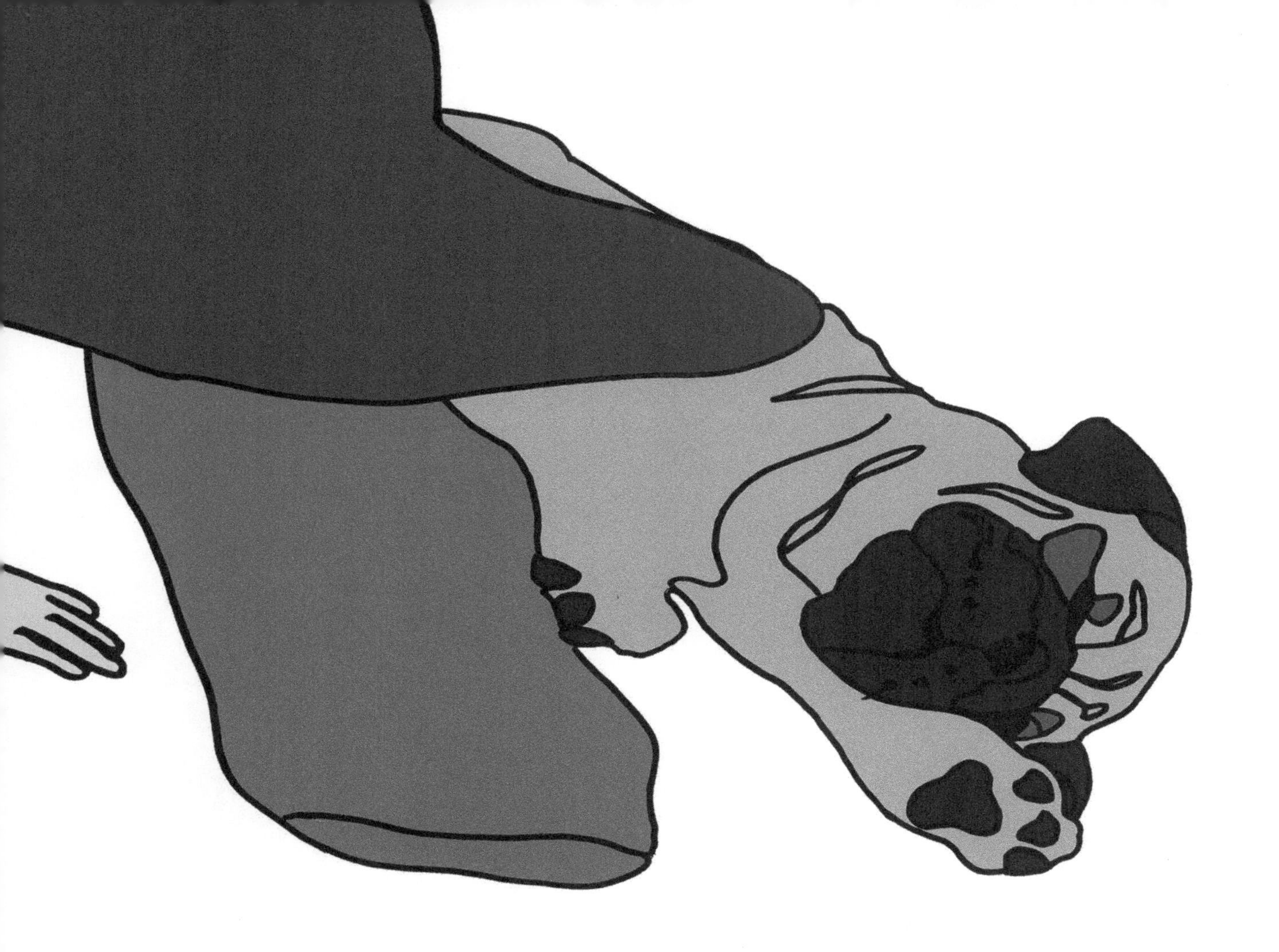

Make time for lots of rest and relaxing on the couch, in bed and even in a super fluffy pillow fort on the floor.

Visit **parks** and **playgrounds** often.

Give pugs extra time to walk, explore and stop to sniff everything. Their noses are smooshed so it takes them longer to smell the flowers, the grass and other dogs.

Talk to your pug and ask about their day.

Look into their googly eyes and tell them stories and funny jokes. Pugs love a good knock-knock joke.

5

Feed them their favorite foods.

Pugs are known to beg for scraps. Especially salmon, bacon and ham sandwiches. But try and fill their bowl with healthy kibble made just for small dogs.

Stretch with your pug.

Get on the floor and do some doggy yoga. It's important to keep your pet active and in good shape. Try some pug moves like...

Give your pug lots of pats and scratches. And hugs.

Pug hugs are the best. Make sure to say things like "good dog" and "who is my smoochy woochy nuzzle bug?"

Make sure they have lots of lovies, stuffies and other soft toys to shake around and drool on.

You'll know when they've found one they really like because they'll sleep with part of it in their mouth.

Make sure your pug has plenty of room to **snore**.

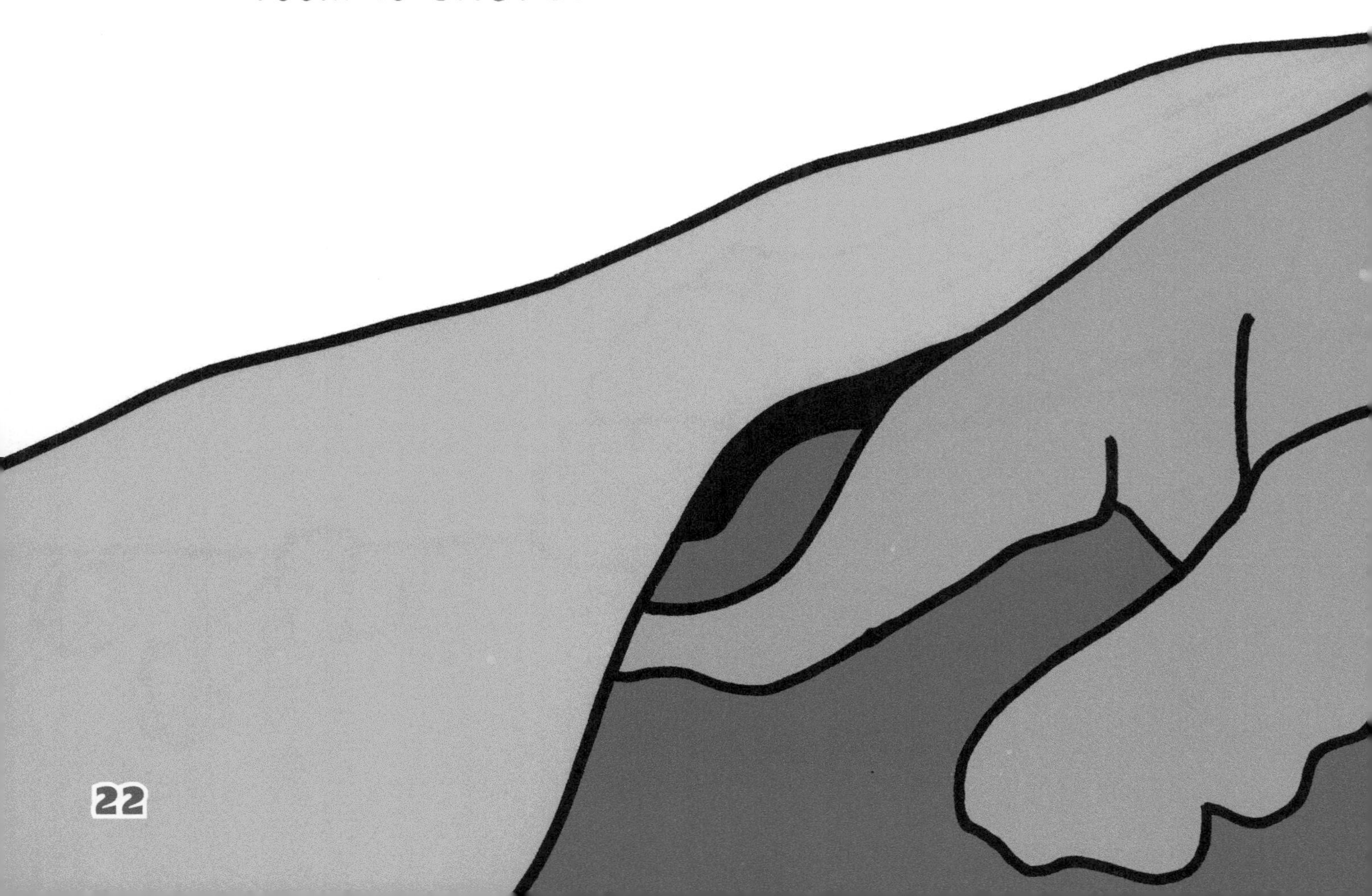

Pugs are loud sleepers and like to burrow under the covers to dream.

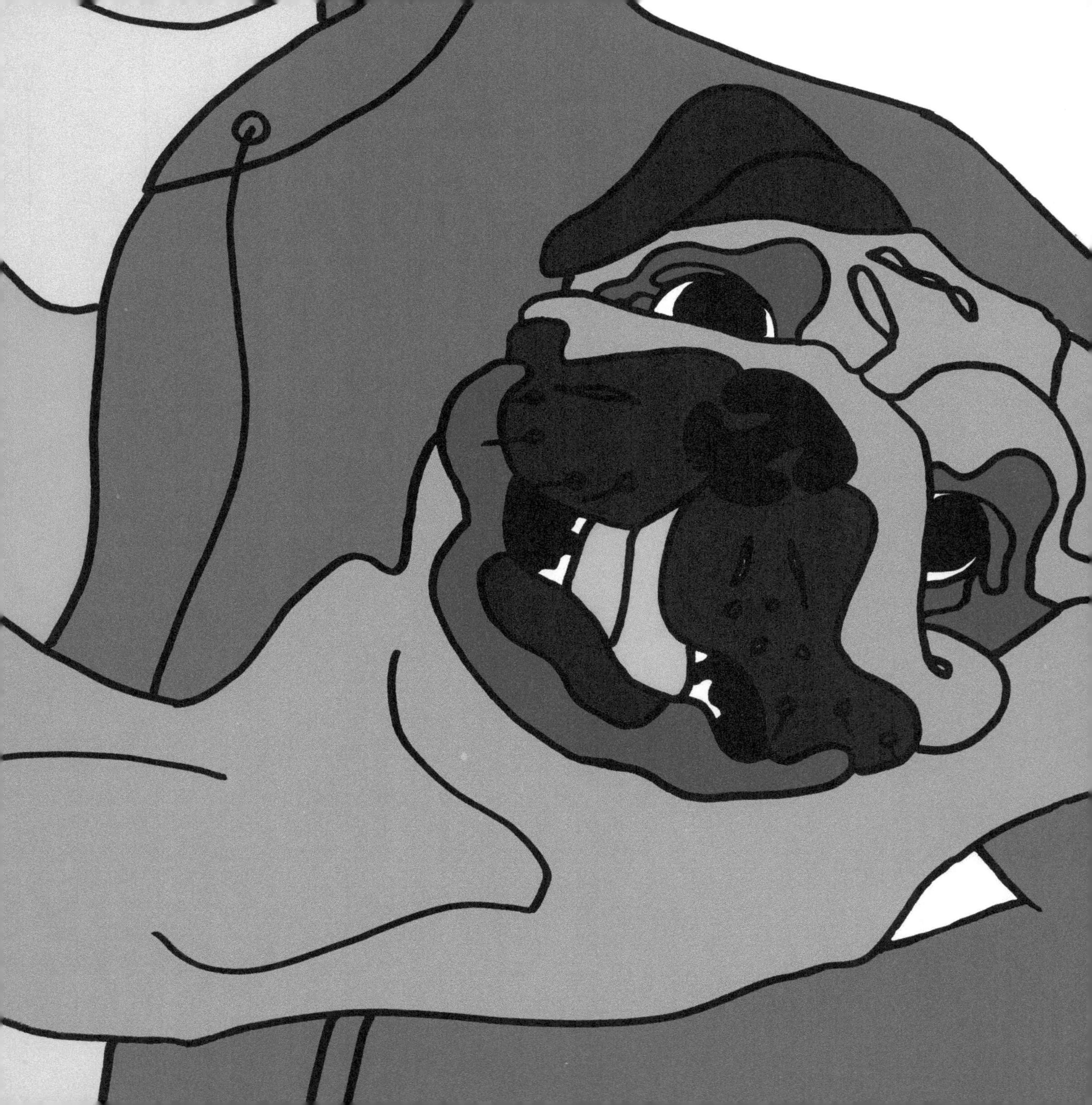

Finally, the most important rule for taking the very best care of your pug...

is to say, "I love you."

Each and every pug day.

ABOUT THE AUTHOR

Lisa Blake is a freelance writer and editor based in Breckenridge, Colorado. When she's not penning family guidebooks, children's stories and articles on wellness and food, she's out playing in forests and on rivers with her husband, son and Mojo the pug.

ABOUT THE ILLUSTRATOR

Nadine Rebrovic is an artist who splits her time between Denver and Breckenridge. Aside from illustrating children's books, Nadine creates custom pet portraits. She started out drawing dogs, but has moved onto cats, birds and even a goat.

CPSIA information can be obtained
at www.ICGtesting.com
Printed in the USA
LVHW070319070421
683636LV00002B/2

9 781647 042745